Brian Ogden was for many years a teacher and RE adviser for the dioceses of Peterb[...] author of more than 50 books, including many titles in the Barnabas range. These inclu[...] *Assemblies*, *Starting Together*, *Beyond the Candle Flame*, *Sing a Song of Seasons*, the ever-popular *Nursery Rhyme Nativities* and, most recently, *Our Easter Play*. Brian is a regular speaker in schools, preaches in the North Norfolk Methodist circuits and is grandfather to ten grandchildren.

Text copyright © Brian Ogden 2010
Illustrations copyright © Marie Allen 2010
The author asserts the moral right
to be identified as the author of this work

Published by
The Bible Reading Fellowship
15 The Chambers, Vineyard
Abingdon OX14 3FE
United Kingdom
Tel: +44 (0)1865 319700
Email: enquiries@brf.org.uk
Website: www.brf.org.uk
BRF is a Registered Charity

ISBN 978 1 84101 606 1

First published 2010
10 9 8 7 6 5 4 3 2 1 0

Acknowledgments
Scripture quotations are taken from the Contemporary English Version of the Bible published by HarperCollins
Publishers, copyright © 1991, 1992, 1995 American Bible Society.

A catalogue record for this book is available from the British Library

Printed in Singapore by Craft Print International Ltd

Our CHRISTMAS PLAY

An easy-to-perform nursery rhyme play for Christmas

Brian Ogden

Acknowledgment

With thanks to Pat Willis for the provision of the puppet-making ideas and instructions in the section 'Using simple puppets in drama'.

CONTENTS

INTRODUCTION

Our Christmas Play contains an easily produced play for use with Foundation/Reception and Key Stage One pupils. The traditional Christmas story is told with rather more emphasis on Joseph than is normally found. The play starts and ends in Joseph's carpentry workshop.

THE NARRATION

A key feature of this short drama is enjoyment. It should be a happy experience without too much emphasis on a perfect production. In the play, the story is recounted through narration, mime and singing. It cannot be emphasised too strongly that the narration is one of the most important features of the play. There may be a temptation to use 'good readers', but more often than not even 'good readers' cannot be heard, and the presentation will be spoiled by inaudible narration. For this reason, it is essential that an adult acts as narrator.

THE PRESENTATION

Christmas is a time of year when a special celebration is appropriate. The play may be used as part of a whole school presentation, as a class or year group assembly, as a school production with parents and visitors present, or as a celebration in church. The songs may be used on their own as a part of other assemblies during the run-up to Christmas. This is a good way of learning them and teaching them to other children.

THE SONGS

The five songs are all written to popular tunes and it has always been found that children learn the songs very quickly. All the words and music have photocopying permission, so there is no problem in providing the words of the songs to all attending any sort of performance. The participation of the audience is a vital and enjoyable aspect of the play, which both encourages the children and helps to generate a sense of sharing in the experience. In some places, in addition to the scripted songs, it is suggested that seasonal carols or recorded music are used.

THE CHILDREN

Schools come in different sizes! *Our Christmas Play* is designed for use with either large or small numbers of children. Older children may be formed into a supporting choir. Younger children can mime the drama as indicated by the narration.

STAGING, COSTUMES AND PROPS

The word 'stage' has been used throughout to indicate the acting area. If possible, there should be access from either side. All movement is given in the stage directions, which are shown in italics.

Decisions over the use of costumes and props must be made locally but the safety of the children is of prime importance. Traditional biblical costume can be simply suggested through the provision of pieces of fabric, dressing-up items, simple cord belts and so on. The two friezes or collages can be organised as a class project, using large sheets of sugar paper or lengths of paste-free lining wallpaper and paint or collage materials. Alternatively, they can be designed in the way of stage 'flats' and simply painted.

PUPILS' WORK

The children might be encouraged to write their own verses to some of the songs. There are a number of places where pupils' own work can be incorporated, including the making of the friezes, drawing items for the things Joseph made, making and colouring the outlines for the sheep, camels and star, and making gifts to represent gold, frankincense and myrrh.

THE PLAY

The story for the play is based on the narratives in the Gospels of Matthew and Luke. Where the actual words from the Bible are used, they are taken from the Contemporary English Version.

THE NATIONAL FRAMEWORK FOR RELIGIOUS EDUCATION

At Foundation Stage the play contributes to the following early learning goals identified in the Framework:

- Personal, social and emotional development
- Communication, language and literacy
- Knowledge and understanding of the world
- Creative development

At Key Stage One the play contributes to many of the requirements, especially the following:

1b name and explore a range of celebrations, worship and rituals in religion.

1d explore how religious beliefs and ideas can be expressed through the arts.

2a reflect on and consider religious and spiritual feelings, experiences and concepts such as worship, wonder, praise, thanks, concern, joy and sadness.

2d reflect on how spiritual and moral values relate to their own behaviour.

3f story: how and why some stories are sacred and important in religion.

3g celebrations: how and why celebrations are important in religion.

3n using their senses.

3o using art and design, music, dance and drama to develop their creative talents and imagination.

USING SIMPLE PUPPETS IN DRAMA

Celebrating Christmas with children provides an opportunity to bring together the whole school, families and friends. Sometimes, however, with the very best of intentions on everyone's part, the celebration can be distracted by the logistics of organising costumes, learning scripts, coping with absences, sharing rehearsal time in the hall and trying to fit everything into the curriculum.

An alternative approach to the celebration is to use puppets—not small hand-sewn glove puppets, which require specific skills and can be very labour-intensive, but simple stick puppets like the ones used so effectively by many Eastern European cultures.

These stick puppets can be easily varied in size and everyone in the class can be involved. They are so simple to operate that they are appropriate for even the youngest or least dextrous child. The process really can be almost instant. Very successful workshops have been held where a large group of children have created their puppets, improvised sounds, movements and music and put on a performance, all within a day.

Depending on the age of the children, you can choose to have an adult storyteller with the children illustrating the story with their puppets. The children can embellish the action by adding their own sounds as they go along. With older children, one member of the class could be the storyteller or each puppet could act out a script devised earlier.

The puppets are not contained in a formal puppet theatre. The performances are in the open. Two large tables covered with a cloth, with simple props to add atmosphere, make a perfect stage.

Art and craft periods can be used to create props, such as a simple stable, manger, inn and so on. A frieze background can be painted, with everyone adding cut-out houses, hills, sheep and so on. To set the scene, the backdrops can be stretched between two bamboo canes and held by stage managers.

Performances can be staged on a conventional platform or worked in the round, with each child bringing their character into the centre in turn while the remaining children in the circle make music appropriate to the action. Instruments might include drums for marching soldiers, and bells or gentle shakers for the angels. The children can also sing or recite.

In order to describe the basic puppet-making process most clearly, instructions for making a shepherd are given below. These will give specific measurements and guidance but they can be easily adapted for any other character or size, by the use of different materials and working to a different scale.

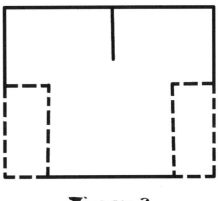

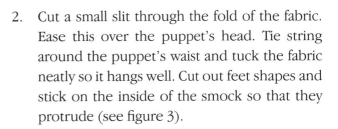

Figure 2

INSTRUCTIONS

1. Lay out the fabric square. Shape stuffing into a ball at least the size of the child's fist and wrap it around the end of the stick. Put this into the centre of the fabric square. Use the elastic band to gather the fabric around the end of the stick (see figure 1). Use some string to tighten neck (B) if necessary. Gather string tightly near end of A and C to make hands. Take a piece of striped fabric 20cm wide and 40cm long. Fold it in half so that you have a double 20cm square. Cut away a sleeve shape (see figure 2).

2. Cut a small slit through the fold of the fabric. Ease this over the puppet's head. Tie string around the puppet's waist and tuck the fabric neatly so it hangs well. Cut out feet shapes and stick on the inside of the smock so that they protrude (see figure 3).

Figure 3

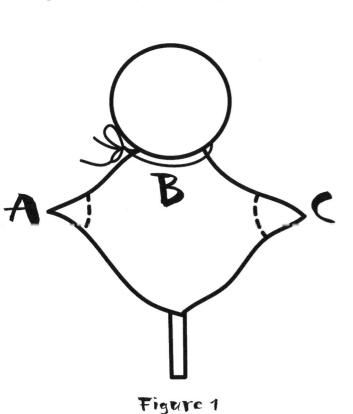

Figure 1

Reproduced with permission from *Our Christmas Play* published by Barnabas 2010 (978 1 84101 606 1)

3. Take a bundle of wool lengths approximately 20cm long. Be sure the bundle is thick. Tie two pieces of the same coloured wool loosely around the middle of the bundle (see figure 4). Lay this bundle over the puppet's head and, using PVA glue, attach the wig to the head. Take a head covering 20cm by 15cm and secure it over the hair with string.

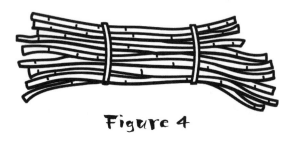

Figure 4

4. At this point, make the features on the face. If they are added earlier, they are invariably covered by hair or headdress. Eyes, nose and mouth can be drawn or stuck on using felt shapes or buttons. The latter is usually more successful as you can experiment with the best position before gluing.

Mary, Joseph, kings and angels can all be adapted from this pattern by using appropriate fabrics and headdresses, such as lace, satin and net.

To work the puppets, the children hold the stick in their non-dominant hand. With their dominant hand they can then move one of the puppet's hands, thus enabling it to hold props, such as crooks or lambs in the case of the shepherd.

Much older children can use broom handles and much larger fabric squares to make almost lifesize puppets. These are very dramatic.

Ensure that the children let the audience see the puppets' faces. Shy children will often perform happily through their puppet as they realise that the focus is away from them and upon their creation. With younger children, using an adult storyteller allows for adapting the story to cover unexpected events—such as the wonderful moment in a nativity production when a tiny sheep came flying over a screen with the cry, 'You forgot your lamb!'

The frieze or backcloth can be wall-mounted in the classroom with the puppets displayed beneath, thus extending the festival project.

A very wise puppet master once said that if you give children scissors that really cut, glue that really sticks, a selection of inspirational recycled materials and an idea for a character, they will amaze you. Enjoy your celebrations!

Figure 5

Reproduced with permission from *Our Christmas Play* published by Barnabas 2010 (978 1 84101 606 1)

OUR CHRISTMAS PLAY

BIBLE LINK

The story is taken from Luke 1:26–38; Luke 2:1–20; Matthew 2:1–15 and Matthew 2:19–23.

Cast

(in order of appearance)

Narrators 1 and 2

Joseph

Children to hold up pictures of what Joseph made

Mary

Roman soldier with proclamation

Children to act as a crowd

Innkeepers

Shepherds

Children to play sheep

Angel (may be a bright light and a voice from off stage)

Angel choir if required (not essential)

Wise men

Servants

Jesus as an adult

Numbers are variable for crowds, innkeepers, shepherds, sheep, angels, wise men and servants.

Props

Woodworking tools or other indications that the scene is a carpenter's workshop

Pictures or objects of what Joseph made

Background frieze of the journey to Bethlehem

Baby doll to represent the baby Jesus

Box to represent the manger

Cut-out sheep masks

Background frieze or collage of journey for the wise men

Cut-out star suspended from the end of a bamboo cane

Cut-outs of sheep and camels

Gifts to represent gold, frankincense and myrrh

The scene is a carpenter's shop. Joseph is pretending to saw a piece of wood. Children hold up pictures of the items that Joseph makes. (The list can be amended.)

Narrator 1:   Joseph was a carpenter who lived in a village called Nazareth.

Narrator 2:   Joseph was a busy carpenter who made…

Children enter one at a time with objects or pictures.

Child 1:   … doors for houses…
Child 2:   … and chairs to sit on…
Child 3:   … and windows to see through…
Child 4:   … and beds to lie on…
Child 5:   … and mangers for animal food…
Narrator 2:   … and a hundred and one other things.

SONG ONE

Joseph was a carpenter

(Tune: Here we go round the mulberry bush)

The children put down their objects or pictures and make appropriate actions as they sing.

> This is the way he chopped down trees,
> Chopped down trees, chopped down trees,
> This is the way he chopped down trees,
> In Nazareth in the morning.

> This is the way he sawed the wood,
> Sawed the wood, sawed the wood,
> This is the way he sawed the wood,
> In Nazareth in the morning.

> This is the way he planed the wood,
> Planed the wood, planed the wood,
> This is the way he planed the wood,
> In Nazareth in the morning.

> This is the way he hammered nails,
> Hammered nails, hammered nails,
> This is the way he hammered nails,
> In Nazareth in the morning.

Children leave after the song.

Narrator 1:   Joseph, the carpenter, was engaged to be married to Mary.

Narrator 2:   One day, when Joseph was busy making a table, Mary came to see him.

Mary enters.

Narrator 1:   'Joseph, please stop banging and sawing for a moment,' Mary said.

Narrator 2:   Joseph put his hammer down.

Narrator 1:   'Joseph,' said Mary, 'I have something very important to tell you. I have just met an angel.'

Narrator 2:   Joseph was listening very hard now.

Narrator 1:   'The angel told me that I am going to have a very special baby. God has chosen me to be the mother of his Son.'

Narrator 2:   Joseph could hardly believe what Mary was saying.

Narrator 1:   'The angel said we must call him Jesus.'

Narrator 2   Joseph was very surprised by this news. But he believed that what had happened was God's doing.

Mary and Joseph leave the stage.

Narrator 1:   Mary and Joseph got married. Several months later, someone else came to Nazareth.

Narrator 2:   This time it wasn't an angel. It was a Roman soldier.

The Roman soldier enters one side and Mary and Joseph enter opposite with other villagers.

Narrator 1:   The soldier came with a message from Augustus, the Roman Emperor.

Narrator 2:   'Emperor Augustus demands that you go to your family towns to be registered. Everyone in the Roman Empire must be counted. These are the orders of the Emperor.'

Narrator 1:   'Mary,' said Joseph, 'this means that we must travel to Bethlehem, our family home.'

Reproduced with permission from *Our Christmas Play* published by Barnabas 2010 (978 1 84101 606 1)

Narrator 2:   The baby was due to be born and they had a long way to go. It was not an easy journey for Mary and Joseph.

All except Mary and Joseph leave the stage.

SONG TWO

Travelling

(Tune: Oh dear, what can the matter be?)

As the song starts, the background frieze is held up and Mary and Joseph travel in front of it.

> Oh dear, what can the matter be?
> Miles to travel to Bethlehem city,
> Joseph tells Mary they must take it steadily,
> Bethlehem's miles away.
>
> We're travelling slowly; the road is quite hilly,
> It's warm in the day, but the night-time is chilly,
> But we cannot stop, we must go willy-nilly,
> It's nearly our son's birthday.
>
> Oh dear, what can the matter be?
> Miles to travel to be with our family,
> Joseph tells Mary they must take it steadily,
> Bethlehem's miles away.
>
> There's not far to go now, a warm bed is calling,
> The sun has gone down and the darkness is falling,
> But look at the people, the crowds are appalling.
> Be quick, our son's on the way.
>
> Oh dear, what can the matter be?
> Miles to travel to be with our family,
> Joseph tells Mary they must take it steadily,
> Bethlehem's miles away.

Mary and Joseph arrive. Enter lots of children. Mary and Joseph have to push their way through the crowd of people.

Narrator 1:   Joseph and Mary reach Bethlehem. They have had to travel slowly and the city is full of people.
Narrator 2:   They must find somewhere to stay. Their special baby will soon be born.
Narrator 1:   Joseph tries to find them a room, but all the inns are full.

A line of innkeepers come on. Joseph goes to each in turn and asks if there is any room. As he approaches each one, they shake their head. The last one takes Mary and Joseph to the area set aside as the stable.

Narrator 1:   One innkeeper, kinder than the rest, told Joseph about his stable.
Narrator 2:   'It isn't much,' he said, 'but at least it will be warm for the baby.'
Narrator 1:   And Jesus, Son of God, light for the world, was born in a stable.

Mary and Joseph exit with baby Jesus. Enter shepherds who sit in a semicircle facing the audience. Allow enough space for sheep to come in front.

Narrator 2:   Meanwhile, high on the hills above Bethlehem, some shepherds sat talking and watching their sheep.

SONG THREE

Song of the sheep

(Tune: One man went to mow)

Enter sheep, one at a time, up to ten in total, to the following song.

> One sheep went to graze, went to graze a meadow,
> One sheep and her lamb—baa!
> Went to graze a meadow.
>
> Two sheep went to graze, went to graze a meadow,
> Two sheep, one sheep and her lamb—baa!
> Went to graze a meadow
>
> Ten sheep went to graze, went to graze a meadow,
> Ten sheep... ... one sheep and her lamb—baa!
> Went to graze a meadow.

A very bright light shines and frightens the sheep, which scatter, baa-ing loudly. The light flashes around the shepherds.

Narrator 1:   High in the sky an angel appeared.

Reproduced with permission from *Our Christmas Play* published by Barnabas 2010 (978 1 84101 606 1)

Narrator 2:   The shepherds were terrified.

Narrator 1:   'Don't be afraid,' said the angel.
'I have good news for you—news that will make everyone happy.'

SONG FOUR

Song of the angels

(Tune: London Bridge is falling down)

Angels may come on to sing if required but otherwise the song is sung as the shepherds listen.

Son of God is coming down,
Coming down, coming down,
Son of God is coming down,
Alleluia!

Christ is born in Bethlehem's town,
Bethlehem's town, Bethlehem's town,
Christ is born in Bethlehem's town,
Alleluia!

Peace on earth to everyone,
Everyone, everyone,
Peace on earth to everyone,
Alleluia!

Narrator 2:   The angels went away as suddenly as they had come.

Narrator 1:   It was dark on the hillside now.

Narrator 2:   Then the shepherds started talking.

Shepherd 1:   He is the Son of God!

Shepherd 2:   Dressed in baby clothes!

Shepherd 3:   Lying on a bed of hay!

Shepherd 4:   Born in Bethlehem!

Shepherd 5:   News to make everyone happy!

Shepherd 6:   I'm going to find the baby.

Shepherd 1:   So am I.

Shepherd 2:   Me too!

Shepherd 3:   Count me in.

Shepherd 4:   Try to stop me!

Shepherd 5:   And me.

Shepherd 6:   Off we go!

Narrator 1:   And the shepherds ran down the hill into the city.

The shepherds go off stage to reappear in the stable area. Mary, Joseph re-enter with baby Jesus.

Narrator 2:   It didn't take them long to find the baby, wrapped up warmly, fast asleep in a manger.

Narrator 1:   Mary and Joseph looked very surprised when the shepherds burst in.

Narrator 2:   The shepherds knelt in front of the baby.

Shepherds: This is Christ the Lord!

The shepherds stay kneeling for the reprise of Song Four.

Narrator 2:   The shepherds sang the song of the angels as they worshipped the baby.

SONG FOUR REPRISE

Song of the shepherds

(Tune: London Bridge is falling down)

Sung by the shepherds softly before they leave the stable.

Christ is born in Bethlehem's town,
Bethlehem's town, Bethlehem's town,
Christ is born in Bethlehem's town,
Alleluia!

Peace on earth to everyone,
Everyone, everyone,
Peace on earth to everyone,
Alleluia!

Narrator 1:   The shepherds returned to their sheep. They never forgot the angel or the baby.

The shepherds exit, as do Mary and Joseph with the baby. The wise men and servants enter. A frieze or collage for the wise men should be held up across the back of the stage.

Narrator 2: Meanwhile, crossing the desert, were some wise men.

Narrator 1: These were men who studied the stars. They had seen a bright star in the eastern skies.

Narrator 2: They believed that a bright star meant the birth of a king. They were travelling to find this king.

SONG FIVE

Song of the wise men

(Tune: She'll be coming round the mountain)

The song can be sung and acted by any number of wise men. A large and bright star should be suspended from the end of a bamboo cane. The star will lead the procession round the stage. Child-sized cardboard cut-outs of camels will add humour to the song.

They'll be following a bright star when they come,
They'll be following a bright star when they come,
They'll be following a bright star,
following a bright star,
They'll be following a bright star when they come.

They'll be riding grumpy camels when they come,
They'll be riding grumpy camels when they come,
They'll be riding grumpy camels,
riding grumpy camels,
They'll be riding grumpy camels when they come.

They'll be crossing sandy deserts when they come,
They'll be crossing sandy deserts when they come,
They'll be crossing sandy deserts,
crossing sandy deserts,
They'll be crossing sandy deserts when they come.

They'll be bringing gifts for Jesus when they come,
They'll be bringing gifts for Jesus when they come,
They'll be bringing gifts for Jesus,
bringing gifts for Jesus,
They'll be bringing gifts for Jesus when they come.

They'll be worshipping the baby when they come,
They'll be worshipping the baby when they come,
They'll be worshipping the baby,
worshipping the baby,
They'll be worshipping the baby when they come.

Narrator 1: After a lot of adventures, the wise men found the baby Jesus in Bethlehem.

The wise men kneel before Mary, Joseph and baby Jesus. They present their gifts as each gift is named.

Narrator 2: The bright star had led them to God's superstar.

Narrator 1: The wise men brought gifts for the baby king.

Narrator 2: Gold…

Narrator 1: … frankincense…

Narrator 2: … and myrrh.

Narrator 1: There was no star to guide them home but they had met with Jesus, the light for the world.

As the wise men leave in one direction, so Joseph and Mary leave with the baby in another.

Narrator 2: Joseph took his family to Egypt for a time before returning to Nazareth.

Narrator 1: It was there that Joseph taught Jesus how to be a carpenter too.

Narrator 2: And Jesus grew into a man.

SONG ONE REPRISE

Jesus was a carpenter

(Tune: Here we go round the mulberry bush)

The scene is back in a carpenter's shop again. The grown-up Jesus leads the children as they make the appropriate actions to the song.

This is the way he chopped down trees,
Chopped down trees, chopped down trees,
This is the way he chopped down trees,
In Nazareth in the morning.

This is the way he sawed the wood,
Sawed the wood, sawed the wood,
This is the way he sawed the wood,
In Nazareth in the morning.

This is the way he planed the wood,
Planed the wood, planed the wood,
This is the way he planed the wood,
In Nazareth in the morning.

Reproduced with permission from *Our Christmas Play* published by Barnabas 2010 (978 1 84101 606 1)

This is the way he hammered nails,
Hammered nails, hammered nails,
This is the way he hammered nails,
In Nazareth in the morning.

Narrator 1:   And, through wood and nails on
                the cross, when he was grown up
                Jesus—God's own Son—opened his
                arms wide and invited everyone to be
                friends with God for ever.

The drama may end with the singing of a
traditional carol or all present singing the final
reprise of Song Four below.

SONG FOUR REPRISE

Song of the angels

(Tune: London Bridge is falling down)

Peace on earth to everyone,
Everyone, everyone,
Peace on earth to everyone,
Alleluia!

THE END

Reproduced with permission from *Our Christmas Play* published by BRF 2010 (978 1 84101 606 1)

APPENDIX ONE

OUR CHRISTMAS PLAY SONG LYRICS

JOSEPH WAS A CARPENTER

(Tune: Here we go round the mulberry bush)

This is the way he chopped down trees,
Chopped down trees, chopped down trees,
This is the way he chopped down trees,
In Nazareth in the morning.

This is the way he sawed the wood,
Sawed the wood, sawed the wood,
This is the way he sawed the wood,
In Nazareth in the morning.

This is the way he planed the wood,
Planed the wood, planed the wood,
This is the way he planed the wood,
In Nazareth in the morning.

This is the way he hammered nails,
Hammered nails, hammered nails,
This is the way he hammered nails,
In Nazareth in the morning.

Song Two

TRAVELLING

(Tune: Oh dear, what can the matter be)

Oh dear, what can the matter be?
Miles to travel to Bethlehem city,
Joseph tells Mary they must take it steadily,
Bethlehem's miles away.

We're travelling slowly; the road is quite hilly,
It's warm in the day but the night-time is chilly,
But we cannot stop, we must go willy-nilly,
It's nearly our son's birthday.

Oh dear, what can the matter be?
Miles to travel to be with our family,
Joseph tells Mary they must take it steadily,
Bethlehem's miles away.

There's not far to go now, a warm bed is calling,
The sun has gone down and the darkness is falling,
But look at the people, the crowds are appalling.
Be quick, our son's on the way.

Oh dear, what can the matter be?
Miles to travel to be with our family,
Joseph tells Mary they must take it steadily,
Bethlehem's miles away.

SONG OF THE SHEEP

(Tune: One man went to mow)

One sheep went to graze, went to graze a meadow,
One sheep and her lamb—baa!
Went to graze a meadow.

Two sheep went to graze, went to graze a meadow,
Two sheep, one sheep and her lamb—baa!
Went to graze a meadow...

Ten sheep went to graze, went to graze a meadow,
Ten sheep... ... one sheep and her lamb—baa!
Went to graze a meadow.

Song Four

SONG OF THE ANGELS

(Tune: London Bridge is falling down)

Angels may come on to sing if required but otherwise the song is sung as the shepherds listen.

Son of God is coming down,
Coming down, coming down,
Son of God is coming down,
Alleluia!

Christ is born in Bethlehem's town,
Bethlehem's town, Bethlehem's town,
Christ is born in Bethlehem's town,
Alleluia!

Peace on earth to everyone,
Everyone, everyone,
Peace on earth to everyone,
Alleluia!

Song Five

SONG OF THE WISE MEN

(Tune: She'll be coming round the mountain)

They'll be following a bright star when they come,
They'll be following a bright star when they come,
They'll be following a bright star, following a bright star,
They'll be following a bright star when they come.

They'll be riding grumpy camels when they come,
They'll be riding grumpy camels when they come,
They'll be riding grumpy camels, riding grumpy camels,
They'll be riding grumpy camels when they come.

They'll be crossing sandy deserts when they come,
They'll be crossing sandy deserts when they come,
They'll be crossing sandy deserts, crossing sandy deserts
They'll be crossing sandy deserts when they come.

They'll be bringing gifts for Jesus when they come,
They'll be bringing gifts for Jesus when they come,
They'll be bringing gifts for Jesus, bringing gifts for Jesus,
They'll be bringing gifts for Jesus when they come.

They'll be worshipping the baby when they come,
They'll be worshipping the baby when they come,
They'll be worshipping the baby, worshipping the baby,
They'll be worshipping the baby when they come.

OUR CHRISTMAS PLAY MUSIC NOTATION

Song One

Joseph Was A Carpenter

(Tune: Here we go round the mulberry bush)

Song Two

TRAVELLING

(Tune: Oh dear, what can the matter be?)

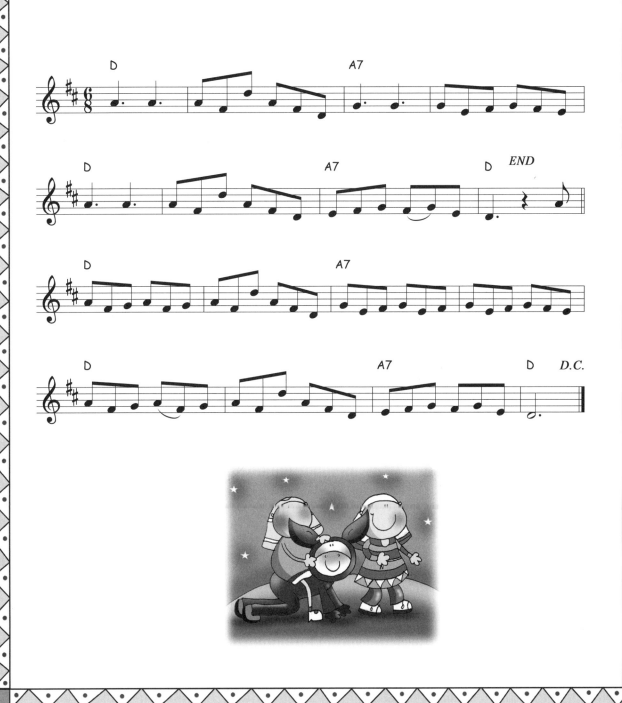

Reproduced with permission from *Our Christmas Play* published by Barnabas 2010 (978 1 84101 606 1)

Song Three

SONG OF THE SHEEP

(Tune: One man went to mow)

Song Four

SONG OF THE ANGELS

(Tune: London Bridge is falling down)

Reproduced with permission from *Our Christmas Play* published by Barnabas 2010 (978 1 84101 606 1)

Song Five

SONG OF THE WISE MEN

(Tune: She'll be coming round the mountain)

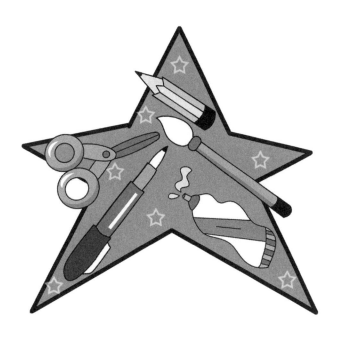

APPENDIX THREE

CRAFT TEMPLATES

SHEEP OUTLINE TEMPLATE

STAR TEMPLATE

CAMEL OUTLINE TEMPLATE